C000103200

BORN BLIND
The Traumas and the Triumphs

BORN BLIND
The Traumas and the Triumphs

DAVID Y. BLOCK

ReadersMagnet, LLC

Born Blind: The Traumas and the Triumphs
Copyright © 2023 by David Y. Block

Published in the United States of America
ISBN   Paperback: 979-8-89091-277-0
ISBN   Hardback: 979-8-89091-288-6
ISBN   eBook: 979-8-89091-278-7

All rights reserved. No part of this publication may be reproduced, stored in a retrieval system or transmitted in any way by any means, electronic, mechanical, photocopy, recording or otherwise without the prior permission of the author except as provided by USA copyright law.

The opinions expressed by the author are not necessarily those of ReadersMagnet, LLC.

ReadersMagnet, LLC
10620 Treena Street, Suite 230 | San Diego, California, 92131 USA
1.619. 354. 2643 | www.readersmagnet.com

Book design copyright © 2023 by ReadersMagnet, LLC. All rights reserved.

Cover design by Jhiee Oraiz
Interior design by Dorothy Lee

TABLE OF CONTENTS

INTRODUCTION

Dear Reader,

The five stories you are about to read in my book titled, Born Blind: Traumas and Triumphs, represent critical parts of my life, feelings, observations, and analyses that marinated inside me long before they reached the written page. Although only one- My father ... Me, and sister Josefina - is non-fiction, the others reflect reality, based on my experiences and those of people I know.

I have been visually challenged since birth, struggling through a lifetime of limitations marked by schoolmates who mocked me and teachers who lacked empathy. Most important, my blindness caused my father to feel disappointed, angry and out of his depth.

I hope that what I've written will help you understand what life is like for people like me for whom every day is one with significant challenges. I want each story to hit a nerve, to make you think and maybe impact the way you treat others and live your life.

Let me give you more insight into "My Father, Me, and Sister Josefina," in which I want to convey that despite the disturbing relationship I had with my father, one that irreparably damaged me, I was able to shine a light into his psyche and come to understand his vulnerabilities.

On a trip to the Philippines with him, he told me he did not know how to be a good father to me and that my partial blindness was difficult for him to handle. That admission was one of the best moments I've had with him as my father. It was one of the few times I ever heard him list his shortcomings. That's what made it a special moment for me.

My story, "You Can't Do Nothing," is dedicated to my friend, John Sutton (1960-2021). John and I met when we were students at Philadelphia's Overbrook School for the Blind in 1969. But we didn't get to know each other well, and after my transfer out of the school in 1970, we had no contact for 19 years.

We met again when he and I travelled from Philadelphia with the PA Association of Blind Athletes to compete in the southern regional games for the Blind in South Carolina. John was living in subsidized housing, but he looked and smelled like a homeless person. (After he died, I learned that he was afraid to bathe due to a terrible experience he had during childhood. One of his closest friends told me that his mother abused him so badly that caused his blindness.)

When we had to register for the games, he told the coach that he could not write his name. All he could do was sign the letter "x." An hour later, he asked me to make his bed because he had no idea how to do that. As the weekend progressed, he confided that his father always told him, "You can't do nothing." By 1983, he and his family severed their relationship.

When I returned from South Carolina, I couldn't stop thinking about John. Writing "You Can't Do Nothing," was the only way I could keep from crying.

His death made me so sad that I ended up making a documentary about him called, "How Sweet the Sound."

"*Ten Minutes to Race Time*" is based on two female USA blind athletes, Pam McGonigle and Maureen Ryan Esposito. When Pam ran cross-country in junior high and high school, she returned home with scratches and cuts because she could not see the thorny bushes on the cross-country trails. To keep her mother from worrying, she quickly changed into long-sleeved pants and shirts.

Maureen was an excellent cross-country runner in high school. But during one race, she got lost and veered off in the wrong direction. Ten members of the opposing team followed her, assuming she knew where she was heading. They were wrong and, as a result, lost the race. Ironically, Maureen's partial blindness contributed to her high school winning the meet.

I dedicate "Ten Minutes to Race Time" to Pam and Maureen. Because they allowed me to interview them, and because they shared these stories with me, I learned a lot about them and also learned that they viewed their partial blindness as an inconvenience, not something terrible. Because of Pam and Maureen, I was able to write "Ten Minutes to Race Time."

"Watch Me" is dedicated to Carlos Talbott, a legally blind Paralympic gold medalist. In 1994, the 37-year-old Talbott was fatally struck by a car during a training run in Florida. His fully sighted partner was not fast enough to keep up with him and prevent the accident. When I interviewed the partner, he told me that if he could have run fast enough to be right next to Carlos, he would have been able to pull him out of the way.

Six years later, I had the misfortune of witnessing a totally blind sprinter, Joe Aukward, run into a fence and break his ribs during the 2000 Paralympic Track and Field Time Trials in New London, Connecticut because his guide failed to keep up with him. These incidents made me think about how difficult it is for many fast blind and sight-impaired runners to find guides as fast as they are and who could ensure their safety. This serious problem still exists and compelled me to write about it.

Finally, "I'm Not a Bad Person" introduces the reader to, and even promotes understanding of a thoroughly despicable person. The character is based on two people I knew when I attended a school for students with learning and social challenges.

You might say I was fortunate in that several students in my gym class and on my bus were more disabled than I. Consequently, they became the school bullies' favorite targets, a fate I escaped most of the time. It struck me, even then, before I had any thoughts about becoming a writer, that the insouciance of those in charge—the teachers, the bus drivers, contributed to the violence I witnessed.

They saw the victims as weak, often unable to read and write and with no promise for the future. They grew tired of having to stop the bullies who tormented them. I never picked on or made fun of those people, but when I saw and heard them being terrorized, I was just grateful that I was being left alone. Witnessing this everyday eventually disturbed me so much that I had to write about it.

I dedicate "I'm not a bad person" to people who were bullied and who were unable to fight back.

While life is difficult for so many of us, we need to be grateful for our strengths. Yes, being able to see is a gift. So is the ability to walk, to hear, to speak clearly. We are luckier than we realize.

I have so many people in my life to be grateful for. I want to thank Gloria Hochman, my editor, who helped me make my stories compelling.

I owe a special debt of gratitude to the renowned actress/publisher Kathryn Leigh Scott, who wrote the forward for this book. One of her many accomplishments was that she starred in the original soap opera horror series, Dark Shadows, which aired on ABC from 1966-1971.

I met her at one of the festivals where she told me about her brother who lost his eyesight. Over the years, Kathryn encouraged me to follow through with my dreams of making documentaries and writing books.

I will never forget Randy Silverman, whom I met at the University of Pittsburgh in the fall of 1983. (I was a Pitt student from September 1983 - December 1984.I then transferred to Bard college and graduated from there, May 1988.)

Randy was my first friend at Pitt - and part of that semester my only friend. He enjoyed reading some of my short stories. His interest in my work gave me the confidence to stick with my writing no matter what other people told me. Although I have not seen Randy since I left Pitt, I will always be grateful to him.

Some close friends and family members helped me revise my early drafts and encouraged me to see this project through to fruition. They also helped me deal with personal problems. Without them, life would have been unbearable. These special friends are Michael Trudgeon, Stephan Shelanski, Marian Leahy, and Joseph Bernstein. I also owe a huge thank you to my family, particularly, my mother Barbara Block, my three sisters, Rachel (Rosa), Shira, and Deborah, my uncle Dan, and his wife Nettie.

Thank you for being in my life. I love all of you.

Finally, I am thankful that God gave me the ability to share these stories with the world.

David Yehuda Block

July 21, 2023

FOREWORD

by Kathryn Leigh Scott

I've long admired David Block's work as a filmmaker and am pleased he's turned his formidable narrative talents to a collection of short stories. His subject matter generally pertains to navigating life in a world that presents significant challenges for someone blind or partially sighted. That's the case with these five stories based on his own experiences and observations as someone who is legally blind.

David writes with fury, compassion and uncommon insight about human experiences we can all relate to, but that have devastating consequences for someone with limited vision.

These are stories of heartbreak that will absolutely break your heart. Don't look for platitudes or happy endings; sometimes things in real life just don't work out with a cinematic feel-good conclusion.

Only one of these stories is nonfiction—a trip to the Philippines with his father, in which David recounts "the disturbing relationship" he had with his father, that he says "irreparably damaged" him. His father's unexpected admission that he didn't know how to deal with his son's blindness helped David understand the man's failings as a father. Still, recognizing his father's vulnerabilities can't undo the years of slights and barbs David endured in a difficult childhood. One cannot read this story without marveling at David's hard-won resilience and determination to achieve his own creative goals and become the man he knew he could be.

His fictional stories are all based on reality; raw truth that can be unbearably dark but shines a light on what it's really like to find one's way in this world without having eyesight.

Kathryn Leigh Scott

May 2023

TEN MINUTES
TO RACE TIME

By David Yehuda Block

"Ten Minutes to Race Time! Ten Minutes to Race Time!" boomed a deep voice over the intercom.

Renee Randalski had heard those familiar words before, but today, they sounded like music. For months, Renee had fought vigorously to become a member of the Drabin High School's cross-country team. She had a lot to prove. In most respects, Renee was like any other high school freshman—with one critical distinction - Renee was partially blind. Coach Elizabeth Dunbar, several of Renee's teammates, and especially her parents were apprehensive about her running cross-country. But Renee knew she could do it and it was time everyone else knew it, too.

But now, she needed to be alone, step back for those next ten minutes, and reflect.

For the past few weeks, Renee had been nervous about this upcoming triangular meet, but she had managed to replace her anxiety with calm anticipation... until an hour ago. A last-minute scenario she never could have imagined sent her heart racing and her body quivering.

The visiting cross-country teams from Drabin and Anderson arrived at Pennwood 's racecourse. About an hour before cross-country races start, whether they are at the pre-high school, high school or at the collegiate level, the visiting teams walk the course so that they do not get lost during the race.

Renee felt fine as she walked the first mile of the three-mile racecourse, but then something unexpected happened that upset her. The guide announced that they would have to run the second mile on an alternative field due to last-minute construction.

"This won't be a problem for any of you," said the guide. "Just follow these arrows. You won't get lost."

This announcement did not bother any of the runners - except Renee. She wanted to scream. She could barely see these arrows.

Usually, she would walk through unfamiliar cross-country courses several times before the race with a friend or with her brother. That strategy prevented her from running the wrong way. Now she felt scared. For a brief minute, Renee thought about just following the other runners. But that wasn't an option. She was faster than most of them.

Oh God, she thought, why did this have to happen on the day my mother is coming to watch me run? Her mother's persistent reminders echoed in her head:

"I love you and I don't want you to get hurt!" Unbidden, an arsenal of warnings from the coach and from some teammates came flooding back: "Are you sure you can run cross country? How can you run if you can't see well? I don't think you know the course well enough. Maybe you had better sit this one out." She remembered the first day of school when Coach Dunbar said, "If you bump into anyone or have an accident, forget about running on the team."

Now her secret would be exposed, Renee thought. Her worst fear—getting kicked off the team because she could not see—was about to happen.

Renee's thoughts flipped back to her first day at Drabin, the first school she attended where she was the only student with a vision problem. Formerly a student at Sutton School for the Blind where she attended middle school, she ached to see how she could adjust to a public school.

She had hated being a student at Sutton. She hated the sheltered environment. She hated not being "normal." She had made no neighborhood friends because none of them went to her school. And she **really hated** that Sutton didn't have after school sports. She knew that as an adult she would have to navigate in a sighted world. Why not begin in high school?

From the start, her experience at Drabin had been a good one. Her schoolbooks were available through two agencies: Recording for the Blind and Dyslectic, and the Library for the Blind. Her monocular allowed her to see the blackboard. But all she could think about from that first day on was her desire to join the school's cross-country team. She remembered standing in front of the coach's office, summoning the courage to enter. She finally did.

"I'm Renee Randalski," she introduced herself, struggling to keep her voice from trembling.

"I know who are, dear," the coach responded. "The faculty was told that a visually handicapped freshman would be coming to the school."

Renee cringed. Why did they have to announce her presence to everyone? Wasn't she entitled to a sense of privacy?

"Can I help you with something?" the coach asked.

"Miss Dunbar," she responded, "I want to try out for the cross-country team."

The coach stared at her quizzically, then fired a series of questions:

"How well can you see? What does it mean to have 20/400 vision? Do you think you can see well enough to keep up with my girls?"

Renee answered those questions, but it sounded as though the coach did not believe her.

Renee was frustrated, but was determined to control her temper.

"Can you at least let me try out?"

The coach continued peppering her with a barrage of concerns.

"Suppose you trip and hurt yourself and your parents sue the school? Suppose you run into someone and hurt them? Suppose there is a car coming and nobody is close enough to warn you?"

"I can take care of myself," Renee countered. "I've run through the woods many times. I've been running for five years, and I never had an accident. I memorize the courses. I see well enough to know if a car is coming. How dangerous can this be?"

"For anyone with normal vision, it's not," responded the coach. "In your case, it's different."

Renee glared and persisted, "No, it's not. And I'll prove it this afternoon if you'll just give me a chance."

Renee reached into her pocket and handed coach Dunbar a note from her doctor saying it was okay for her to run.

Coach Dunbar read the words slowly.

This is to verify that Renee Randalski has enough vision to participate in after school sports. Her visual acuity is 20/400, which means what you can see from 400 feet away, she can see the same things, but from 20 feet away. I have seen other sight-impaired people play sports alongside their perfectly sighted peers. If you have concerns, please call my office.

After what seemed like an eternity to Renee, the coach lifted her head, looked straight into Renee's eyes and said, "Okay, you can run at the time trials today. If you meet the requirements, I'll need a note from your parents and permission from the principal that it is okay for you to run on the team."

"To make the team, "continued the coach, "you have to run one mile in under six minutes and 30 seconds. Then, with very little rest, you will have to run the three-mile cross-country course in less than 23 minutes. If you don't meet both requirements, you can't be on the team, and you won't get a second chance to try out this season."

Renee smiled. "I can meet those requirements. I'll see you after school."

As Dunbar watched Renee walk out of the office, she wondered how this half-blind girl could be so audacious.

When Renee arrived for the time trials after school, there were about 15 girls warming up and stretching. They wondered what she was doing there.

Finally, the team captain, Colleen Robinson, stood up. "Are you lost? Can I help you?" she asked.

"No, I'm not lost," answered Renee. "I'm trying out for the team."

"Do you think you can handle it?" asked Colleen. "How can you run if you can't see well?"

"I know what I'm doing." Renee responded. She wanted to tell this girl to mind her own business.

Instead, she just sat apart from the other girls and stretched. She had no desire to talk to anyone.

The other girls continued stretching and talking about which boys were hunks, and which boys were geeks, occasionally glancing in Renee's direction.

Coach Dunbar jogged to the field. She briefed the squad about the time trial requirements and then turned to Renee. "Be careful on the track. Run into anyone - forget about joining the team."

Renee took her place at the starting line. The one-mile time trial race began, and Renee took off with the leaders. As Renee ran neck and neck with Colleen, ahead of everyone else, the coach thought that this half-blind girl would use up all her energy before the second lap.

Renee stayed with Colleen until the last fifty yards, when the senior sprinted ahead. Renee wished that she had a kick like that. The freshman finished the mile run in five minutes and 50 seconds, just 20 seconds behind Colleen.

Running the cross-country course was a "piece of cake" for Renee. Colleen finished first, the co-captain finished second and Renee finished third; her finishing time was 20 minutes and 44 seconds. The rest of the runners trailed Renee by one minute.

"So I made the team?" Renee asked the coach.

Coach Dunbar hesitated. "It's a big risk. Some cross-country courses are very dangerous. I'll have to talk to the principal. There may be problems with insurance and the school's liability because of your condition. You may have to sign a waiver."

Renee shot back, "I beat more than half your team! I proved I could do this. If I tell my parents, you won't let me on the team, they'll say it's discrimination."

That night at dinner, Renee told her mother about making the team. All she needed now was written permission, but her mother refused to give it.

Later that night, Renee convinced her brother Tommy to swipe a piece of their mother's stationery, write a note giving Renee permission to run on the team, and forge their mom's signature. Renee presented the note to Coach Dunbar the next day.

The principal shared the coach's reservations but acknowledged that the school had no choice. "What can we do?" he said. "She meets the requirements, she has permission from her parents and her doctor. Let's give her a chance to prove herself."

Until a few days ago, Renee's mother had no idea that her daughter was on the Drabin High School cross-country team. But then she found out when she saw Renee's picture in the local paper wearing her high school cross country attire. The photo was part of an article about how Renee, a sight-impaired person, was able to run so well.

Her mother was furious and threatened to ground her.

"I know you want to protect me," Renee told her parents," but I wish you would trust me. I've been on the team for about three weeks, and I haven't gotten hurt or lost. I'm one of the fastest runners they have. They need me."

"She's happy when she runs with the team," interjected her brother. "You ought to see her. She's never looked happier. Why don't you watch her run in the next meet? You'll see that there is nothing to worry about."

"Five minutes to race time!" The announcement jarred Renee back to the moment. Some of her teammates were still jogging along the field. Renee ran past them.

"Two minutes to the start of the race," boomed a deep voice on the intercom.

All the teams assembled at the starting line. The coaches briefed the teams on the racecourse. "Take your places!" yelled an official.

Renee felt her knees tremble.

"Fifteen seconds! Ten seconds! "Five seconds. Four - three - two - one - GO!"

Renee took the lead.

"Don't go so fast, Renee," yelled Coach Dunbar.

Renee ignored her. She ran hard and fast, up the first hill. She ran down the road, then turned into a field. She wasn't sure if there were any ditches. She heard runners behind her. Where were those directional arrows?

The runners gained on her, so she picked up the pace, while taking quick breaths. Renee sprinted ahead. The pace was a little too fast for her, but she had to win.

After about ten minutes, she sensed that something was wrong. She knew that she had run further than a mile, but where was the guy at the one-mile mark who shouted out the times? She turned around and saw about ten runners from the Anderson High team following her.

"Which way do we go?" one of them asked.

"I don't know. Did you see the arrows?"

"We didn't see any. We were following you."

"I can't see arrows, I'm half blind."

"You little bitch," yelled an Anderson runner, "you led us the wrong way on purpose because you knew your team couldn't beat us."

"Bullshit! I wouldn't need to cheat to beat you. It wasn't my fault we got lost. I'm half blind, I can see the orange cone markers, but I can't see arrows."

"You're lying! You just wanted to make us lose!"

"It was an accident! If your vision is so damn perfect, how come none of you saw the arrows?"

Silence.

"Well, let's not argue. Let somebody else lead and let's find the damned course."

They eventually got back on course, and Renee took the lead. But Renee and her group of followers were the last runners to finish the race.

"What took you so long?" barked coach Dunbar as Renee crossed the finish line.

"Don't ask, but look who's behind me!" She turned and pointed to the Anderson runners.

Renee walked over to Dunbar. "Am I still on the team?"

"If it's okay with your mother, it's okay with me."

"It's fine with me", said Renee's mother.

Renee smiled. The war was over and she won.

"I wouldn't be smiling if I were you," the coach continued.

"Why?" asked Renee. "We won."

"When we get back to Drabin, you're going to run 25 laps around the track. My policy is Anyone on my team who gets lost in a race has to run laps. No exceptions." Coach Dunbar walked away muttering, "Of all the stupid things... leading people the wrong way."

"It wasn't that stupid," Colleen whispered to Renee. "This is the first time we ever beat Anderson."

Renee's mistake benefited her team because they finished second out of three schools instead of finishing dead last.

"Have fun," her mother said, almost laughing. "I'll keep your dinner warm. See you when you get home, dear."

As Renee turned to walk with the team, Colleen said:

"This won't be so bad. I'll run the 25 laps with you."

"You won't have to worry about counting the laps," said Coach Dunbar. "I'll watch you run all the laps."

"All because I couldn't see the arrows," said Renee.

The coach said laughing, "No special treatment."

Renee smiled as she and Colleen ran those laps because she now felt like a full member of the team.

WATCH ME

By David Yehuda Block

PART ONE

Albert Godfrey was startled as the oversized numbers on his watch came into focus: 8:30 a.m. He jumped out of bed. His 10K race was going to begin in two hours...and he had neglected to register in advance. Now, he had twenty minutes to wriggle into his running attire and hurry to reach the post-registration line in time. He broke into a sweat, knowing that he would need help filling in the necessary forms. In the past, he had sometimes encountered a surly person at the table: "If you can't see well enough to fill out a form, then you can't see well enough to run...."

At those times, he struggled not to lash out. He had a short temper, cultivated as far back as elementary school. When classmates taunted him about his vision problems, he fought back with his fists calling on the martial arts skills he had learned to defend himself. The bullies always retreated.

He ran up to the registration line, breathless, and tapped the man standing in front of him. "Excuse me, sir," he said nervously. "I don't see too well. Could you please help me fill in the race form? I don't want to hold up the line."

Albert was conscious that the man was staring at his thick glasses. "I see you have a vision problem," he said. "Do your eyes always move like that?"

"Yes," responded Albert, trying not to sound irritated.

The man helped Albert fill in the registration form and guided him to the starting line. He was surprised to see Albert line up with him at the very front. "Shouldn't you go toward the back?" the man asked. "We're going to take the pace out very fast and you'd be in the way. We wouldn't want to run you over."

Albert turned and stared right into the man's eyes. "I'm going to win," he told him. "Watch me."

"Attention runners," boomed a voice over the microphone, "the race will start in 60 seconds. There will be water stations at every mile mark."

A minute later, the announcer yelled, "RUNNERS, TAKE YOUR MARK.SET"

BANG! Went the sound of the loud starting gun.

Albert grabbed the lead immediately, and for the first mile, he listened for the sound of runners behind him. There were no challengers...it felt like a lonely training run. No, he couldn't have made a wrong turn. The pace vehicle was right in front of him...he could smell the fumes.

"One-mile time, five minutes 15 seconds," yelled a man with a stop-watch.

"That sucks," Albert muttered to himself. He knew that he could easily break a 4:55 if someone challenged him.

"Can you see anyone behind me?" Albert asked the man.

"No," the man answered.

Two miles later, a spectator tried to hand Albert a cup of water. "How close is everyone else?" asked Albert.

"No one else is near you."

Albert was happy that he had jogged the course yesterday while his wife, Lynette, rode her bike alongside him, alerting him about where there were potholes and sharp turns. She assured him that the course was an easy one.

Albert ran his fastest for the last mile. Spectators held their hands out offering to shake his. But there was no time for that.

"Finish line, less than a hundred yards," yelled voices in the crowd. "Go, dude. You got it."

Albert crossed the finish line. "Thirty minutes and thirteen seconds." yelled the announcer.

A couple of minutes later, the man who had helped Albert register finished. He was 4th overall.

"You were great," said the man, revealing that his name was George Reynolds. "How about a beer?"

For the first time that day, Albert felt congenial... and relaxed.

"I told you I was going to win," said Albert.

PART TWO

Albert and George became good friends. They often ran together. That made Lynette happy because she could worry less about her husband getting hurt. That had happened from time to time, once when he hurt his ankle stepping into a pothole, another when he collided with a volunteer bringing him a cup of water.

George and other members of a local running club often guided Albert during training runs, but they were too slow for him. Sometimes, especially when he was tense because of a tough day at work, he wanted to relieve the stress by running alone.

This was one of those days.

'I'm going for a run," he told his wife. He said he would be running alone, without George.

Lynette worried because it was getting dark, and she was concerned about a car that Albert might not see.

Breaking out of the house, he headed to a nearby ten-mile course with tough hills. Running the ten-mile course would take him less than an hour.

Lynette was anxious. She grabbed her bike from the garage and followed her husband. She was determined not to let him get hurt. But she had to make sure he wouldn't see her.

Lynette grimaced as she saw Albert approach the course. Those ominous hills and speeding cars! What about the ditches he would not be able to see?

After biking about five miles, Lynette spotted some large potholes up ahead. Albert was heading toward them. She pedaled up to a middle-aged man biking near her and said, "my husband can't see well and he's running ahead of me. He doesn't know I'm here. Could you ride next to him and warn him that he's coming to some ditches?"

The biker nodded. He sped ahead and caught up to Albert. "Be careful," he said. "There's a ditch on your left." Albert passed the ditch safely.

As Lynette watched Albert avoid some cars, her bike hit a pothole and she tumbled off. When Albert heard her cry out, he turned around and ran toward her. After he finished admonishing her for following him, he said, "As long as you're here, do you want to ride alongside me for the last five miles?"

Lynette gladly accepted his invitation.

"I think I can keep you from riding over more potholes," he laughed.

"Some day!" she grimaced. She wanted to make a joking gesture of strangling him, but he probably wouldn't see her hands.

Both Lynette and Albert arrived home safely.

PART THREE

"I'll see you in an hour," said Albert as he kissed his wife. "Keep my dinner hot and save some of that chicken for George. Do you want to know where George and I will run in case you decide to follow on your bike? There won't be any potholes, so you don't have to worry about having another accident."

"Give it a rest," said Lynette. "That happened 3 weeks ago. I bet you told George."

"What makes you think I'd do something like that?" Albert laughed.

"He told me the next day," said George.

"You don't need to worry about me," said Albert.

"I'm not worried," Lynette responded. "George is with you."

Albert and George decided to run 10 miles in one hour. They ran the first seven miles in silence. Then Albert had the urge to surge ahead, just a little faster. In a few minutes, the rain began, drizzling at first, gradually coming down faster until puddles covered the ground. There was no avoiding them. The sky darkened. George felt sick as he looked at Albert 50 yards ahead. With one mile to go, Albert and George were running off the path onto the road. Cars zoomed by them as George kept a watchful eye on Albert.

"Why did it get dark so early?" murmured George.

Albert was too far ahead to hear George.

"why did we have to spend so much time talking to Lynette?" George mumbled. "We might have gotten back before the rain."

George looked ahead at Albert.

"Albert, slow the fuck down right now. Wait for me to catch up!"

"What for? I'm feeling great."

The rain was coming down harder now, obscuring visibility.

Albert couldn't see the car coming close to him.

George screamed as loud as he could. "Watch out, Albert! Car coming!"

If it had not been raining, Albert would not have slipped directly into the car's path. The road was too wet and slippery for the driver to stop in time. George shrieked in horror, and he couldn't stop. He knew, in that instant, that his friend and running mate who tried to tell the world that disability does not mean inability, would never utter those words again.

Albert Godfrey was dead.

EDITOR'S NOTE

This story is a tribute to Carlos Talbott, one of the world's best visually impaired runners. Talbott was killed while running, and David Block wrote an article about him for Runner's Gazette in October, 1994. Several days before his death, Talbott had won the Flamingo Strut 8K, clocking 27 minutes and 56 seconds. In 1988, at the Paralympics in Seoul, South Korea, he had set a record in a marathon for visually impaired runners by clocking 2:22:55, and he did the same in the 5K by running 15:09.84. According to the United States Associates for Blind Athletes, no one in the world had yet broken those records.

In January 1993, Talbott met Bruce Jenner (now Caitlyn Marie Jenner) as they ran together at the

American Air Lines Miami Mile, a series of races to raise money for various charities. "I was impressed with what good shape Carlos was in," said Jenner, who had retired from running several years earlier. "He had a good spirit. He kicked my butt."

"Carlos won so many races because he ran harder than anyone else," said his close friend, Ralph Guijarro. "He wanted to show that he was as good as anybody who didn't have a handicap."

YOU CAN'T DO NOTHING.

By David Yehuda Block

From the time Roy Samson was a little boy, his father told him, "Boy, you can't do nothing." Then he would beat him.

Now, Roy was 55, and no matter how hard he tried, he couldn't get his childhood memories out of his mind - specially at Christmas.

There was the Christmas season when his father was painting the house. Roy was just six-years-old.

"Dad, let me help you paint."

"No way! You can't see nothing!"

Roy began to sniffle.

"Go away, Roy. I'm busy."

On Roy's way out of the room, he tripped over a can of paint, spilling its contents onto the new rug.

"Boy, you can't do nothing," his father screamed.

Then came his father's slaps and punches, which Roy knew so well.

"I've been breaking my ass getting this house ready for Christmas, and you messed everything up. I ought to make your ass clean it up…but you can't do nothing."

Three years later, when he was a live-in student at Woodbine School for The Blind, he remembered lying on his bed brooding. It was just before Thanksgiving, and the other children in his dorm were talking about going home.

"I can't wait to go home," said Jim. "My mom is making a big turkey."

"I love my mom's pumpkin pie," said Mike. "My sister says she's getting the first piece this year. No way!"

"Shut up," Roy snapped. "I got a headache."

"No," Mike protested. "You're not my boss. You're just mad because you're not going home for Thanksgiving."

"You're dead!" Roy shot back. Then he dragged Mike from his bed onto the floor and punched him repeatedly. Physical attack was a lesson he had learned well from his dad, and he practiced it on his peers whenever he was angry, which was practically all the time.

The housemother intervened.

"You're always acting up and misbehaving," she berated him.

"No wonder your family doesn't want you home for Thanksgiving. There's something wrong with you."

A couple of weeks later, the school principal, who had heavy footsteps and smoked vile-smelling cigars, entered Roy's classroom. Everyone trembled.

The principal's appearance usually meant that someone had misbehaved and would be taken to his office for the paddle. At the time, teachers and principals were still allowed to hit their students.

The principal cleared his throat. "Roy Samson," he called. "Come with me." Roy's classmates breathed a sigh of relief.

"Why?" protested Roy. "I ain't hit no one today."

"Didn't hit anyone today," corrected the principal. He grabbed Roy's arm and yanked him out of his chair.

As they approached the office, he told Roy, almost gently:

"Relax, Roy. No paddle today. There's a phone call for you. Your mother is on the phone."

After he handed Roy the phone, Roy felt excited. He wanted to tell her that he was trying to be good and that he was glad to come home for Christmas. But as soon as he said 'hello,' his mother cut him off.

"We found out that Woodbine will let you stay for Christmas, so you ain't coming home."

Roy unexpectedly loosened his tight grip on the phone. It almost slipped out of his hand. Cold sweat dripped down his face.

"Why?" he asked.

"It would be a hassle," his mom said. "I don't feel like waiting for you at no bus stop. And you always forget to bring stuff home."

"Mom, everyone is talking about going home."

"Damn it. I don't feel like discussing it no more. I don't know why that damn principal put you on the phone. I said to just give you the message."

"You didn't even want to talk to me?"

"Not today."

"Wait, Mom…"

But all Roy heard now was the dial-tone.

A few tears trickled down his cheeks, but he choked back the sobs. Roy had not cried for over a year after his father had beaten him.

"Stop crying," his father ordered.

"I hate crybabies. Bad enough you're blind, but be a man. I told you before that your mom and me didn't want you. The Lawd cursed us with a blind baby for not getting married first. Now stop blubbering before I whip you some more."

Even his single year of happiness in seventh grade - at age 12 - when he wrestled for Woodbine, ended in disaster. Roy was having a great season. He was undefeated, but his new world of happiness soon ended the day his parents came to see him wrestle.

If he won this particular match, he would be the first Woodbine wrestler in the school's history to win a tournament trophy for his weight class.

Roy was confident that he would win, so was his coach and even his parents. When the whistle blew, Roy ran onto the mat eagerly. He charged his opponent, John Nills, a student he had beaten soundly earlier in the season. As they locked arms, Nills whispered, "I'll kill you."

"Nills, you're a pussy," shouted Roy as he threw Nills to the floor.

"Unsportsmanlike conduct," shouted the referee. "One point, Nills. I don't want to hear that language anymore. "

Above the roar of the crowd, Roy heard his father's voice, admonishing, "Behave!"

The referee blew the whistle. Roy grabbed Nills' arm and head and was preparing to throw him to the mat, but Nills inched his way to the edge and whispered, "When was the last time you took a bath? You can't do nothing."

"You're both too close to the floor. Break," shouted the referee. But Roy flipped Nills onto the floor.

"Another point, Nills," shouted the referee.

As the match progressed, both wrestlers scored takedowns and reversals.

In the third and final period, the two tried to take each other down, but Roy was unaware that Nills was near the edge of the mat. The referee did not say anything. Roy scored the take down, but Nills' arm hit the concrete floor and Roy fell on top of it.

"Fucker!" screamed Nills. The sound of Nills's arm breaking echoed through the gym.

"Disqualification!" shouted the referee. "Off the mat!" He grabbed Roy by the arm and pulled him away.

Roy's wresting career at Woodbine was over. The coach was too nervous about letting him wrestle for him. He thought that Roy was too dangerous and now he refused to let something like that happen again.

The words he had heard all his life kept ringing in his ears. "You can't do nothing."

Now, half a century later, Roy Samson lay in bed listening to the insistent alarm of his talking watch. He stretched his arm across the night table until he reached the watch and turned off the alarm.

Roy was in a hurry to get the day started. He wanted to get to the bank to cash both of his checks—one was his disability check and the other was his meager paycheck from his job at Woodbine Blind School's workshop where he hammered nails and stacked items in containers. That check meant so much more to him than his larger disability one. It was the first job where he earned money, and for once, he felt as though he were like everyone else, rising early and going to work.

He would use the money from his job to buy a new radio. He had that old radio for nearly 20 years, and he was sick of it. Roy tossed his old radio into the trashcan. The sound of it smashing to pieces was sweet.

Roy put on the same unwashed pants he had worn yesterday and the day before. Part of the pant legs looked like ripped string, but how was Roy to know? No one cared enough to tell him.

Roy headed for the bank, his white cane in one hand and a tin cup in the other. At a street corner near the bank, he stopped to sing. This was the primary way he picked up some spare change, but he was tired of singing in the street all the time. On his way, he met a vender who handed Roy a soft pretzel. He knew Roy liked them. "This one's on me," he said. "Merry Christmas."

Roy thanked him and resumed walking to the bank.

Roy was eager to buy his new radio.

He wouldn't have to hear his inconsiderate neighbors, Mr. and Mrs. Jones, throw another one of their Christmas parties.

The apartment building Roy lived in consisted of low-income tenants with disabilities.

After withdrawing his money, he headed for work at the Woodbine School. He couldn't wait to get his hands on a hammer and nails because that task always made him feel better.

When Roy entered the workshop, he knew immediately that something was wrong. What happened to the sound of hammer and nails? What happened to the people laughing?

"Roy," the workshop supervisor called out to him. "If you had a phone, I could have saved you a trip. The administration is having trouble with funding, and the workshop is closed - indefinitely."

"I need this job!" Roy protested. "You know how long I've been singing in the streets? Can you help me find another?"

"It is not easy," she answered. "Tests show that you have a very low aptitude, and right now there's nothing available that would suit you. I'm very sorry. I wish there was something I could do."

Roy left the school, bought a radio and went home. Back in his bedroom, he threw himself down on his unmade bed. Angrily, he flipped through the stations seeking a ball game. Christmas carols polluted his radio and worsened his mood. He punched the wall, hoping to put a dent in it.

"Turn down that radio," shouted his neighbor, Mr. Jones, after Roy had found a talk show unrelated to Christmas.

Roy ignored him.

Next thing Roy knew, Mr. Jones was in his apartment, smashing his new radio.

"That radio has been giving me a headache for two weeks. No more! You're the most inconsiderate neighbor."

"It was brand new!" Roy shouted back. "I'll kill you, mother fucker!"

Jones stepped back when he saw Roy, twice his size, charge him like a bull. He kicked over Roy's trashcan and chair and ran outside. Roy fell over the chair, still screaming that he would kill Jones. Downstairs, the Christmas music was still blaring.

Roy burst into tears. For most of his life, he had taken pride in not crying. Now, he could no longer hold back the tears.

His father was right when he kept repeating to Roy:

"You can't do nothing! You can't do nothing!"

The words rang in his ears. And he believed them.

I'M NOT A BAD PERSON

By David Yehuda Block

I'm not a bad person. Although I've done things that were bad, I'm not a bad person.

I used to terrorize people and I loved it. It was fun. It always made me feel better - a lot better especially after certain nights.... when I was beating up people. I knew I wasn't a bad person. I never raped a child like someone I knew. That someone was my dear "sweet" father and I was his victim.

Several times a week, he'd come into my room after midnight, after my fat drunken mother was asleep and snoring so loudly that our house would almost shake. Then I would hear Dad's heavy footsteps walking toward my bedroom. To this day, many years later, I still shudder when I hear anyone snore loudly or when I hear heavy footsteps.

Whenever Dear Old Dad came into my room, he never wore anything. I'd close my eyes so I wouldn't have to look at his fat stomach and bald head. He got on top of me, did his business and then reminded me that he wasn't a bad person. He reminded me that he gave me a house to live in, three meals a day, a place to sleep. That never made me feel better. Even then I knew that prison provided the same luxuries. I knew this because Dad was in jail several times.

While I was Dad's midnight toy, he was too big for me to fight, but I swore that one day I'd get even with him.

My father warned my mother and me to never - ever - call protective services. If we did, he would have hurt us both in the worst way. At the time, we were too scared of him to even consider the idea. I knew that one day this would all be over. One day, I'd be dead and free of him.

My mother never stopped him from raping me. Worse, she never tried. Sometimes when I complained to her about that or about anything for that matter, she'd respond with

"Why didn't I go to the fucking drugstore that night?" She said that to me many times. It wasn't until years later that I understood what she meant. She wished that I was never born. When I realized that that was what she meant, I went from merely hating her to hating her as much as I hated my father.

For some stupid reason, I thought that maybe she would protect me and love me. Boy, was I naive. It taught me to never trust anyone, never love anyone and that life was war.

When I got older, I realized that I hated my mother for another reason. I hated her for being too lazy to go to the drugstore. If she had, I wouldn't be here.

As I grew older, I grew angrier...which was unfortunate for some of the people I terrorized.

Some of those people were absolutely friendless. They were repulsive to look at, often extremely disabled, and I knew that other people around me couldn't stand them either.

I imagined that my victims wore my father's ugly repulsive face. I pretended that they were my father and that I was punching him while he was terrorizing me. No one did anything to stop him, and, for the most part, no one tried to stop me.

My main victim was Fred, a classmate at Ramsey Elementary School for the emotionally disturbed. Fred was completely normal until he was six-years-old. Fred had fallen off a cliff while hiking with his family. He was in a coma for a few weeks and when he came out of it, he could no longer walk, talk or see properly. Now, he stuttered and slobbered when he spoke. His glasses were so thick that he looked like a freak show. I didn't know him when he was normal. I only knew him when he was my classmate. I didn't care about how he was. I only saw him as someone ugly and stupid like my father.

Before Fred transferred at Ramsey, our teacher, Ms. Hawkins, gave my class a preview of the student who would be joining us the next day. A perfect victim for me.

She told us how Fred fell off the cliff, how his life changed for the worse. The kids, whom he was friends with, now refused to have anything to do with him. He had to leave his last school because his classmates had mistreated him. Ms. Hawkins told us that Fred was scared and that she hoped we would make him feel at home.

We didn't!

He showed up late for class and struggled to open the door, he walked in, with braces on his legs, like a wounded duck...and everyone laughed. He stuttered. There would be more laughter.

For me, Fred was the ideal victim. Helpless, like I was with my father. Fearful, like I was when I heard my father's footsteps at my bedroom door.

It made me feel better to taunt him.

"Did your mother tell you you're a dumb retard?" I asked him that day at recess.

"Leave me alone," Fred would stammer as my classmates and I pelted rocks at him.

"Then go back where you came from," I said, spitting in his eye. "No one wants you here."

I kicked him in the face and he fell to the ground like a tottering tree. I planted my muddy shoe on the swollen part of Fred's cheek where I kicked him. It made me feel good, as though I finally punched my father. Even then I knew down deep that I wasn't a bad person. It was all about getting even.

When the doctor told me and my parents that I had a venereal disease, they pretended to be shocked. But the three of us knew I had gotten it from my father. No one at school or our neighborhood knew that dirty little secret. I remember feeling sick and hating my father and feeling thankful for Fred.

I wanted to hurt my father. I hurt Fred instead. But I'm not a bad person.

Sometimes, I was scared that the kids in my class would pick on me because I had serious reading and math problems. So I was thankful that Fred was there to take the brunt of my classmates' taunts. It kept me safe.

I was happy to see Fred back in school after a month-long absence. I heard that he was sick for two weeks and that he was in a mental for the other two weeks. Five minutes after he arrived, I stuffed mud down his shirt. He looked ugly and gross, just like my father.

Around Christmas time, Fred gave me a football and said, "Merry Christmas. If you like, I can help you with math."

I knew why Fred got me that present and offered to help me. Maybe I would come to realize that he was a nice person and I would stop picking on him. Maybe I would become his friend.

What Fred didn't know was that I couldn't help myself. Even when I knew I was doing bad things, something inside me wouldn't let me stop. I kept seeing my father's face looming above mine his ugly, grotesque face. When I looked at Fred, he dissolved into father. We were all losers—my father, Fred, and me.

I know that some of the things I do are not very nice. But I'll keep on doing them. Deep inside where I'm afraid to look because I don't know what I'll find, I know I'm not a bad person.

EPILOGUE

When I was 16, I attacked my parents. It took me 16 years to finally muster up the courage to do that and it felt great. I had no regrets, not even when I was arrested and shipped to a juvenile detention center where I spent the next two years.

My parents and I never wrote each other. In fact, I never saw my parents again and I hope I never will.

I wanted to find Fred. I wanted to tell him I was sorry. I wanted to make it up to him. I felt so guilty. But I never found him.

I finally learned what happened to Fred when I ran into a former Ramsey classmate at a drugstore.

The classmate told me that Fred killed himself. What upset me even more was when I learned the reason why he took his life.

The classmate told me that Fred was too scared of people. He was afraid to go outside because he was scared to death that someone was going to beat him up.

Then the classmate said:

"Fred was so scared, but he wasn't afraid to jump in front of a moving train."

I walked away and out of nowhere I cried. I never cried that much in my life, not even when my father used to rape me, not even when I understood why my mother regretted not going to the drugstore.

I never tried to visit any member of Fred's family…I couldn't face them. What was I going to say to them?

"Hi, I'm the one who beat up Fred almost every day. I always threw rocks at him and loved it."

I never went to Fred's grave to pay my respects. I knew what would happen. I'd start crying and I wouldn't be able to stop.

All I could do was remind myself that although I've done things that were bad, things that were hateful, I'm not a bad person.

Even though I still hear my father telling me each time he raped me, "I'm not a bad person," I know I'm better than my father. I never raped a child and I never wanted to.

Fred's suicide made me realize that I was capable of caring about people.

I'm not a bad person. Although I've done things that were bad, I'm not a bad person.

MY FATHER ... ME, AND SISTER JOSEFINA

By David Yehuda Block

My father and I never got along. I was not the son he wanted. He was not the father I longed for. My memories are shaped by his unrelenting criticism, his taunts about my inadequacies, his refusal to participate with me in any father-son activities. When I would ask him to do something simple such as showing me how to throw a football, he would look away and respond, "I'm too busy."

He was busy reading a newspaper.

You see, I am partially blind. Kids at school had trouble accepting me. Some even taunted me.

But I always thought that parents fully accepted their children and supported them no matter their weaknesses or disabilities. In my case, I was wrong.

My father lashed out at me for climbing the stairs too slowly, for walking clumsily, later for missing a spot shaving. "Do you know how much I paid for you to have special glasses?" he would remind me. "I could have gone to Europe with that money."

Until I was in my late teens, I thought my father's outbursts were the symptoms of a bad temper. Just before I entered college, I learned the truth from my mother. She told me that to my father, I was a disappointment. If I couldn't throw a pass in football, run the bases in baseball or deliver a punch, I was not macho enough to meet his standards.

It reflected negatively on him to have produced such a son.

My father's approval was important. I yearned for him to be proud of me. The first time The New York Times published an article I wrote, I hoped this might be a turning point. For a short time, I thought it was. My father was impressed that The Times sent me a check for $150.00; he stopped what he was doing and made copies of the check. But his pride was short-lived.

He told me about a week later that he did not care about the articles I was writing or the documentaries I was creating.

It gave me little comfort to have learned from my mother that her father-in-law told her shortly after she met him that his son was worthless. She said that my father, Sy Block, spent his life trying to get his father to like him. He failed miserably. That was my father's role model. Maybe he thought that all fathers were supposed to treat their sons that way.

Nonetheless, I saw my father as a good man. I didn't want to be his friend, but underneath it all I loved him, and I wanted him to love me. I think he wanted only the best for me. But he told me once that he did not know how to deal with my blindness. He went onto tell me that he did not know how to be a good father.

When I heard my father tell me this, I was moved. I personally thought that sharing these admissions with me was his best moment as my father. I admired his honesty and his willingness to share his shortcomings.

In my early twenties, my father expressed his concern about me not having girlfriends. I'm not gay. I never was and I never will be and my father knew that, too. But my lack of action with women upset my father probably almost as much as it upset me. This was another example of me not being macho.

"I worry about you," he told me. "When I was half your age, I had girlfriends. What's the matter with you?"

My father hit a nerve, and I think he knew it.

It bothered me just to see couples hold hands. Even love songs made me sad because they reminded me of my awkwardness with girls and what I was missing out on.

I recognized that my father cared about me. Had he not cared, we never would have had those conversations.

Then came our disaster in the Philippines. During summer break in college, my father decided that he and I would travel together to see a faith healer in

The Philippines, Sister Josefina, a woman who had mysteriously improved my uncle Dan's vision. After he saw her, he could see traffic lights more clearly and he no longer had to press the cards to his face when he played 500 Rummy.

I had often asked my father to take me to her, but he had ignored my pleas...until the time that his blood pressure climbed to dangerous levels with doctors unable to help him. Now he thought there was a reason for both of us to visit Sister Josefina.

We arrived after a harrowing ride with Francisco, a driver my father had hired to take us to the mountain-town of Baguio where Sister Josefina lived. It was about a four-and-a-half-hour drive from our Manilla hotel. It was a blistering summer day, the car didn't have air-conditioning, and my father was especially disagreeable.

We did not have Sister Josefina's address, and she did not know we were coming.

Our driver could take us only to a bumpy gravel road a mile or two from where he thought we might find her.

"From here we have to walk," he told us. My father's disposition grew testier. After trudging down a narrow path in unbearable heat, we ran into some Filipino men. Francisco pointed to us and said something in Tagalog.

"Yes," answered one of the men. "She is here. Follow me."

A long walk later, a woman approached us.

"Good day, gentlemen," she said. "I am Sister Josefina." It was difficult to see what she looked like because the glaring sun affected my already limited vision. She began speaking:

"I work for 25 consecutive years, then I rest a year," she told us. "The Holy Spirit commands it. This is a rest year."

My father snapped, "We need help; we came all the way from the United States just to see you."

Sister Josefina told us to relax. Because we had travelled so far, she was permitted to make an exception.

I still remember her saying those things just as clearly as I remember the setting. The heat drenched my clothes. Flies buzzed in my ear. Nearby, children were playing with animals I failed to recognize.

Schools were closed because during the spring and early summer parents needed their children to help them in the fields. After June 21, the children were back in school. In that respect, summer was like our Autumns in the U.S.

A child led us to a hut which was Sister Josefina's chapel. There was silence except for the buzzing flies and the sounds that came from the animals.

"I enjoy seeing Sister Josefina," Francisco told us. "She makes me happy. God bless her."

A young looking man approached us.

"Right now, Sister Josefina is praying for you. You must pray too."

"Who are you?" I asked.

"Her assistant."

I could hear the incessant buzzing of the flies.

The assistant told my father and me:

"Pray."

So I prayed quietly, quiet enough for no one to hear me:

"God, please help me. God, get these damn flies away from me."

When Sister Josefina entered the chapel, I was finally able to see how she looked. She was a corpulent woman with a rotund face and dark hair. She possessed a sweet voice. Her smile was so big that even I could see it. She wore a cross around her neck.

Per her instructions, I removed my shirt and lay on her table. She lit a candle, looked to the sky and chanted a prayer while some of the children rang bells. She rubbed a cold cream in my eyes, then all over my body. An assistant reached for my arm and told me to breathe deeply. Sister Josefina pricked needles into my spine and the back of my neck while the children sang.

She murmured something about getting blood to flow from my pancreas to my brain which would result in blood circulating through my eyes. She whispered, "I will help you. You will see better. Have faith, for He is with you. Pray."

After Sister Josefina "treated" my father, she embraced us; then we walked out into the sunlight, internalizing her instructions not to eat meat, swim, shower, drink alcohol, smoke, exercise or have sex for the next 48 hours. Our primary objective was to thank God and figure out how to become better people.

We didn't follow her mandate. In fact, my father had other ideas about how he was going to salvage this trip which he had already declared was a waste of time and money.

Once back in our hotel room, he called a massage parlor and requested that two girls be sent up.

"You'll thank me," he said as he stepped into the bathroom and splashed water onto his face.

When the women arrived, my father ordered me to take off my clothes. One of the women and I made an attempt at sex. but I couldn't perform. My father, who laid across from me in the other bed, had no difficulty. My sex-partner became impatient, and I became angry. The women finally left.

For the next two days, I was physically ill.

The whole trip was a complete failure.

My eyesight never improved, and my father still struggled with high blood pressure.

I went on to complete my final two years of college.

My feelings about my father zigzagged as did his treatment of me. I was grateful that he was instrumental in identifying Bard as the college that would be the most nurturing for me, and that he paid for my tuition. I was disappointed that he disapproved of my chosen career—writing articles and producing documentaries.

I guess it was because he didn't see it as leading to a money-making future. Nonetheless, he financially supported a couple of my documentaries including "Abandoned Heroes," that went on to win awards at film festivals.

In college and after graduation, I was a voracious reader in spite of my limited sight. I had never learned Braille because my father had withdrawn me from the Overbrook School for the Blind in Philadelphia, insisting that "no son of mine was going to read by learning braille." Before I would listen to books on tape, I insisted on reading them first because I wanted desperately to read like everyone else. My very expensive, very thick, prescription reading-glasses, for which my father paid - allowed me to do that. I devoured James Joyce, Tolstoy, Dostoevsky, and Faulkner.

Soon after graduation from Bard, I became a freelance reporter, my interests and writing focusing mainly on those with disabilities. I wrote about blind athletes, those who had become paralyzed, wheelchair users and others who had made accomplishments despite their limitations.

My documentaries, including "Dancing Outside the Box," and "Who Said You Can't Dance?" which I produced and directed, won awards for best documentary at several prestigious film festivals.

Still, my relationship with my father never became the one I would have wanted. Yes, he did take me to the Metropolitan Opera in New York, but only when he could not find anyone else to go with him. He did give me money to help pay for my mental health treatment when I went through an agonizing depression. At the same time, he understandably reminded me, "I'm not a cash register."

As time went on, I was no longer afraid of my father. When I was little, I was afraid of him because he had a bad temper and was capable of beating me up. As an adult, I was afraid whenever he threatened to never give me another cent. My successes sustained me, and I found a benefactor through one of my cousins. He believed in me, helped support some of my projects and allowed me to gain confidence in myself.

Meanwhile, my father became more frail. Ironically, his vision began to fail after he had a stroke in 2002. He had suffered through and conquered colon cancer, heart failure, internal bleeding, and a brain Aneurysm. He was invincible. Well, that's what I thought until I saw how he reacted to his vision worsening. He refused to go to rehab because he did not want to learn to live like a blind person; he knew that they would not restore his sight.

When he died, on December 2, 2008, I was surprised at how sad I felt. I kept remembering the positives and how, despite his criticism and demands, he had, in many ways, shaped me into the resilient man I have become. This is some of what I said in my eulogy to him:

"The word 'quit' was not part of Sy Block's vocabulary. I try not to let it be part of mine. That was one of the many gifts he gave me. His legacy also included ambition. When he came to this country from Cuba, he asked some of my mother's relatives who lived in the Philadelphia area where the most affluent area to live in would be. When they said, 'Lower Merion,' he was determined to live there… and he made it happen. No matter that he was this Cuban who had just arrived and was practically broke, he was determined. He was driven.

In 1999 and 2001, I had the honor of seeing him receive the award for being the number one salesman for certain insurance companies. No matter that he was over 70, older than the other insurance agents. He was not past his prime. He was Sy Block and he would not allow younger agents to outsell him.

He passed some of that on to me. If he had not been my father, I wonder whether I would have pushed to interview high-powered people. I wonder if I would have allowed my vision problem to discourage me from making documentaries. I might not have done it had I not inherited my father's drive. Thank you, Dad.

Even as far back as college, he inspired me to learn about the Holocaust, and I completed a 94-page project on American writers' responses to Fascism and Nazism during the Third Reich.

My dad loved reading the classics. His favorite book was the Iliad. When we discussed Dante's Inferno, he'd recite the beginning of the poem to me in Italian.

Sy Block inspired me, and I know he wanted the best for me.

A few minutes before he died, I said these words to him. I want to say them again now.

Dad, te Quiero! Vaya Con Dios! Dad, I love you. Go with God."